SAN   WN

A MEAN
FISH SMILE

Also in the Sandwich Poets series

AN ODD KETTLE OF FISH

Poems by John Rice, Pie Corbett and Brian Moses

LOST PROPERTY BOX

Poems by Matt Simpson, Wes Magee and Peter Dixon

ELEPHANT DREAMS

Poems by Ian McMillan, David Harmer and Paul Cookson

SANDWICH POETS

A MEAN FISH SMILE

ROGER STEVENS
SUE COWLING
and
JAN DEAN

Illustrated by
Jane Eccles

MACMILLAN CHILDREN'S BOOKS

First published 2000
by Macmillan Children's Books
a division of Macmillan Publishers Ltd
25 Eccleston Place, London SW1W 9NF
Basingstoke and Oxford
www.macmillan.com

Associated companies throughout the world

ISBN 0 330 39215 8

3 5 7 9 8 6 4 2

A CIP catalogue record for this book is available from the British Library.

Printed by Mackays of Chatham plc, Chatham, Kent.

CONTENTS

Roger Stevens

The End of the World 2
Poem for Sale 3
Cat Message 4
Bat Pet 6
The Last Day of My Holiday 7
The Song of Winter 8
The Estuary Field Trip 9
Lowku Haiku 10
Epitaph to Fred 10
Message for Mum 11
Mobile Home for Sale 12
Assembly Song 13
Smelly People 14
If All the Autumn Leaves 15
Drum Kit for Sale 16
Sing a Song 17
Messages 18
The Supermarket for Lonely People 19
Dragon Love Poem 20
The Winning Goal 21
Walking the Dog Seems Like Fun to Me 22
My Step-dad is an Alien 24
Shelley 26
I'll Miss My Gran 27
Don't Miss the Boat 28
What Teacher Does at Night 29
Who Says a Poem Always Has to Rhyme? 30

Sue Cowling

What I Like About Ice **32**
Winter and Summer **33**
Wintercolours **34**
The Void **35**
The Huntress **36**
Boy **37**
I Can't Think Straight! **38**
River **39**
The Painter's Diary **40**
The Seashell's Prayer **41**
Haiku **42**
Aphrodite **43**
On the Fifth Day … **44**
Missing **45**
Pillow Monsters **46**
Wanted **47**
Rehearsals Rule – OK? **48**
Ghoul School Rules **49**
Cleopatra **50**
Shocked! **51**
The Sweep **52**
Icicle **53**
Ass **54**
Limerick **55**
Midnight Feast **56**

Jan Dean

It's Not What I'm Used To **58**
Waiting For **59**
Granddad in the Garden **60**
Private Rock Pool – KEEP OUT! **61**
Beluga, Beluga **62**
Torches in the Wood **63**
Sweets from Strangers **64**
Who's There? **66**
Nightmare **67**
Shadow Places **68**
Ssh ... [a poem for two actors.] **69**
Chinese Water Torture **70**
Temptation **72**
Their Secret is Out! **73**
Cold Fish **74**
The Unit of Sleep **75**
The Rubber Plant Speaks **76**
An Owl Flew In My Bedroom Once **77**
Dear Mum **78**
Glass-Eye Charlie **80**
My Sister is Barmy **81**
Heart Stuff **82**
Ghosts in Our Suburban Homes **84**
Angels **86**

Roger Stevens

Roger lives in a shed at the bottom of his mum's garden. He has a wife and three children who visit him sometimes and bring him crisps and chocolates. Most of the time he sits at his computer thinking up stories and poems but occasionally he takes Judy, his dog, for a walk. He loves visiting schools and libraries to perform his poems and talk about his work. His hobbies are playing in a rock band and growing different varieties of moss.

The End of the World

Uncle Bill
Foretold the future.
The future from him
Wasn't hid.
One day he predicted
The world would end.
And for him
It did.

Poem for Sale

Poem for sale
(One careful owner)
With simile,
(As lucky as a dime)
Two exquisite
And erudite adjectives
And one rhyme
Going
For a song

Cat Message

Shemu the cat
Whose ancestors
Prowled amongst the pyramids
Today received a special visitor

Neferhotep
Ambassador
From the constellation of Orion

Upon Neferhotep's
Departure
Shemu tried her best
To warn her mistress
Of Neferhotep's message

The Earth is about to be invaded

Shemu lay on the carpet
And made letter shapes
With her body
I – N – V – A – S – I – O – N

Shemu brought twigs and scraps of bark
Into the kitchen
Arranged in the symbol O-ki-hran
Which is Orionese for
You are about to be invaded by hideous aliens
From the constellation Andromeda

Shemu even reprogrammed the video
To play *Star Trek* tapes
But Shemu's only reward
For her efforts
Was some tinned cat-food

Humans, thought Shemu,
Can be so …
Dumb.

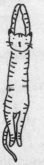

Bat Pet

I have a pet bat
And he lives in the shed
He sleeps when I'm out to play
And plays when I'm in bed.

The Last Day of My Holiday
(a Haiku poem)

When we left Grove Park
My best mate went to one school
I went somewhere else

We arranged to meet
To play tennis in the park
I was kitted out

He lived across town
It was a long, hot bike ride
It would be worth it

I knocked on his door
He's at school, his mum told me
They went back today

As I cycled home
My head buzzed like a beehive
My eyes were stinging

He was my best friend
How could he do that to me?
Just a joke, he said

The Song of Winter

The song of winter
Is sung by the wind
With music so sad the trees share it
The words to the song
Are told by the wind
So sad that the heart cannot bear it

The Estuary Field Trip

I walked with my class along the estuary
The salty wind sneaked through the cracked concrete
of time-worn sea defences,
stirred the weeds and rusty wire
that rose from the caked mud bed.
Thirty children poked under rocks
hunting for crabs
and tugged at a lump of driftwood,
perhaps once part of a sailing barge
taking bricks to London.

Isn't it beautiful? I said
Richard looking at me, nodded, smiled
A rare moment
A mystical union of teacher and pupil
Mr Stevens, said Richard,
Did you see the Man U game last night?

Lowku Haiku

If a poem has
Just sixteen syllables
Is it a lowku?

Epitaph To Fred

Here lies the body
Of stick insect Fred
He never moved much
I hope he *was* dead

Message for Mum

Mum left her mobile phone in the kitchen
It rang and so I answered it
Hello, a buzzy voice enquired,
Star Commander – are you fit?

Battle cruisers in position?
Are the warheads timed and toggled?
Is the laser death-ray charged up?
Have the mind-warp bombs been boggled?

Across vast galaxies we've travelled
With our huge invasion fleet
Now we've found this puny planet
It doesn't look too hard to beat

Across the starfield's endless oceans
Will be heard our victory song ...
Excuse me, I said interrupting,
I think you've dialled the number wrong

I'll take a message if you want
Mum's just popped out to buy some bread
Stupid Earthling – are you joking?
And with that the line went dead.

Mobile Home for Sale

Judy is a delightful
Mobile Home
with Central Heating
a warm Basement
Superb Penthouse Views
and includes luxury
Deep Pile Carpets
in black and white.
Fully Air-Conditioned
by large wagging tail.
This Border Collie
would suit large family of fleas.

Assembly Song

Dance, dance
Wherever you may be
I am the Lord of the Dark Settee
and I'll bounce on you
and you can bounce on me
and we'll all sit down
and watch TV

Smelly People

Uncle Oswald smells of tobacco.
Aunt Agatha smells of rope.
Cousin Darren smells of aeroplane glue.
Cousin Tracey smells of soap.

My mum smells of garlic and cabbage.
My dad smells of cups of tea.
My baby sister smells of sick.
and my brother of TCP.

Our classroom smells of stinky socks.
Our teacher smells of Old Spice.
I wonder what I smell of?
I'll just have a sniff …
hmmm … quite nice.

If All the Autumn Leaves

If all the autumn leaves
In all the world
Were all piled up
Into one big pile
The wind would blow them down our street

Drum Kit for Sale

Drum Kit for Sale
Guaranteed to make house shake
Very Loud Indeed
(Gave Mum a headache.)

Drum Kit for Sale
Snappy snare – terrific tone
Dad says – *Must go at any price!*

(or will exchange
for trombone.)

Sing a Song

Sing a song of ten pee
A pocketful of friends
Four and twenty kind words
Always make amends
When your pocket's empty
Fill it full of smiles
And make sure your friends
Are human beings
And never crocodiles

Messages

At school
when I'm feeling low
I whisper a secret message into my hand
and hold it tightly in my fist
until playtime.
Then I release my message,
watching it soar
like a carnival balloon
into the speckled sky.

At night,
when Mum has turned out the light,
I think of Dad
and I'm sad that he's dead
but I still have the message
he whispered to me.
I pick up the conch shell
by my bed
and listen again.

I hear him,
like the echo of a shooting star
in the seas of space.
Don't worry, he whispers,
I love you.

The Supermarket for Lonely People

Walking along deserted aisles
you'll find
a solitary tin of smiles

Past the pet food
the smell of fresh-baked hugs
hangs in the air

On the shelves sit
bottled-up words of kindness
all wishing they'd been spoken

As you pass through the empty tills
the check-out person
makes you a special offer

Dragon Love Poem

When you smile
the room lights up

and I have to call
the fire brigade

The Winning Goal

When I scored the winning goal
I had never felt so alone
The crowd went crazy, on their feet
But my heart sank like a stone
They say that scoring is marvellous,
The best feeling that's ever been known,
But it's hard to take
When you make a mistake
And the back of the net
is your own.

Walking the Dog Seems Like Fun to Me

Dad said, The dog wants a walk.

Mum said to Dad, It's your turn.
Dad said, I always walk the dog.
Mum said, Well I walked her this morning.
Dad said, She's your dog —
I didn't want a dog in the first place.

Mum said, It's your turn.

Dad stood up and threw the remote control
at the pot plant.
Dad said, I'm going down the pub.
Mum said, Take the dog.

Dad shouted, No way!
Mum shouted, You're going nowhere!

I grabbed Judy's lead
and we both bolted out the back door.

The stars were shining like diamonds.
Judy sniffed at a hedgehog, rolled up in a ball.
She ate a discarded kebab on the pavement.
She chased a cat up a tree.

Walking the dog
seems like fun to me.

My Step-dad is an Alien

I'd suspected it for some time.
I finally got up the courage
to talk to him about it.

I think you're an alien, I told him.

Nonsense, he said. Why do you think that?

You're bald. You don't have any hair
anywhere.

That's not that unusual, he said.

Well, you've got one green eye
and one blue one

That doesn't make me an alien, he replied.

You can make the toaster work
without turning it on

That's just a trick, he smiled

Sometimes I hear you
talking to mum in a weird alien language

I'm learning Greek
and Mum lets me practise on her

What about your bright blue tail?

Ah, he said thoughtfully.
You're right, of course.
So, the tail gave it away, did it?

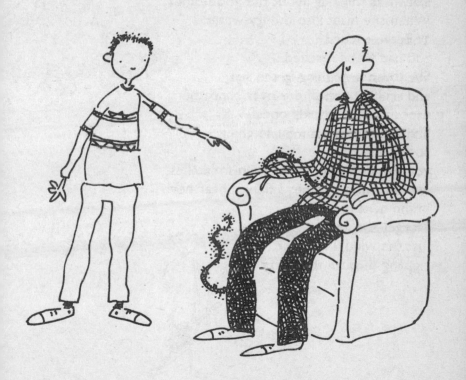

Shelley

I was thinking about my dog,
Shelley.
She died a while ago
but you still remember friends, don't you,
friends who have passed away.
She was unhappy at the end,
confused, she would bump into
the furniture, and stand
staring into the corner of the room.
But I was thinking about the good times.
When she leapt into the icy water
at Betws-y-coed
and had to be rescued.
She loved swimming in the sea
and shaking herself dry over sunbathers,
especially old wrinkly ones.
She was a great one for fetching
sticks and balls –
you couldn't take her to tennis matches.
You know, sometimes I think I hear her
in the next room.
I forget she's gone.
Just the wind, I suppose,
rippling through my memories.

I'll Miss My Gran

My gran's going to die soon.
Mum told me last night,
I suppose it had to happen one day.
I suppose I hadn't thought about it much.

I'll miss her funny stories
about the good old days.

Mum says
we all die sooner or later.
The thing to do
is to have a good time when you're young,
to build up your memory bank
for when you're old.
Then you'll have lots of funny stories
to tell your own grandchildren.

Well, for Mum that might be OK
but I'm not having grandchildren.

No way!

Don't Miss the Boat

The Woebegoing cried big fat tears
as the animals entered the Ark.
He'd been packing his case for thirteen years,
at first for a bit of a lark.
But now, as the animals boarded the ship,
he sat on the bank and bit his lip.

For thirteen years he'd searched the land
looking for a mate.
For thirteen years he'd sifted sand,
but now it was too late.
He rang his bell,

sung

a farewell song
and the Woebegoing
was the Woebegone.

What Teacher Does at Night

When the chalk dust settles
And the children have gone home
And a kind of empty quietness fills the room
The teacher gives a gentle tug
To her hidden plastic plug
And slowly she deflates, like a balloon

Who Says a Poem Always Has to Rhyme?

There was a young man called Frank
Who kept his pocket money in the ...*

When he'd saved enough he bought an electric viola
And celebrated with a can of co ...**

When he plays the viola the whole house rocks
It makes your shoes dance and it frightens your ...***

Frank plays his viola all of the time.
Who says a poem always has to ...****

* Post Office **-conut cordial ***granny ****have a similar sound at the
end of the line as it had at the end of the line before?

Sue Cowling

Sue Cowling has been writing poems since she was nine and has tried to give it up but can't! She writes in bed between six and seven in the morning on bits of paper which sometimes get eaten by her dog. She teaches English to people of other nationalities, has two grown-up children and lives near Birmingham.

What I Like About Ice

The slip and slide and sheen of it,
The dizzy dance-routine of it,
The gleam and glide and glitz of it,
The pointy splintered bits of it,
The glint and gloss and glaze of it,
The crazy-paved parquets of it,
The silly fun-house floors of it,
The icicle-cold claws of it,
The whoosh and swish and shush of it,
The churning into mush of it,
The creak and crack and crunch of it,
The drinks that clink at lunch with it!

Winter and Summer

Winter is quiet and grey.
The streets are wrapped in fog,
Trees shiver,
Birds have flown away.

Summer is loud and green.
Bees bagpipe in the grass,
Leaves quiver,
Birds are heard and seen.

Wintercolours

Scarlet on green?
Ripe berries on a tree.
Dull gold on grey?
The sun's ghost on the sea.
Silver on black?
One star against the night.
And sheep against a snowdrift?
White on white.

The Void

Look into my face
And take a pace
Into a wilderness
Of driftwood, dunes and sand.
A no man's land.

Step inside my head,
Inspect the empty bed,
The room swept bare,
No clue. No mess.
No forwarding address.

Tune into my mind,
Rewind
The silent spools and brush
The bat-winged echoes from your hair.
I am not there.

The Huntress

Barefoot amongst the stars she goes,
Holding the silveriest of bows.
What is she hunting? No one knows.

Close at her heel the shadowhound
Takes constellations at a bound,
Sniffing the spangled hunting ground.

Thickets of stars with steely thorn
Shelter the weak and lately born.
Fly from Diana's shrill, wild horn!

Boy

They cannot cope with him,
The boy who terrorises other children.

When war came
And all the men went off to fight
The boy was left to guard the village.
They gave him a gun
And said "If strangers come,
You shoot them, right?"
He nodded.
He was fourteen.
Late one night
A man stole from the darkness.
Then the boy thought of his promise,
His responsibility.
He aimed, shut his eyes tight
And shot the man
Who was his father. Now
They cannot cope with him,
The boy who terrorises other children.

I Can't Think Straight!

I can't think straight!
    That's good.
    You see,
    You're having
    An attack
    Of poetry.
    So think curly,
    Think cock-eyed,
    Think round corners,
    Round the outside.
    Think criss-cross
    Or in figures-of-eight
    But whatever you do –
    Don't think straight!

River

The river is rushy,
The river is deep,
The river has fishy
Secrets to keep.

The river is khaki,
The river is still,
The river has murky
Pockets to fill.

The river is eerie,
The river is dead.
The river has scary
Rumours to spread.

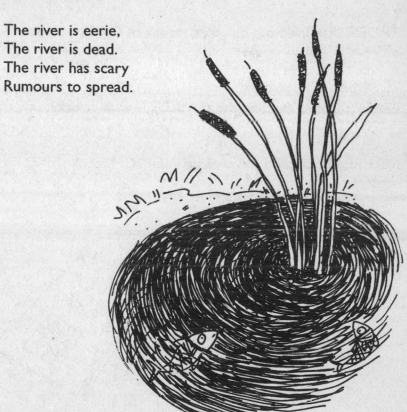

The Painter's Diary

MONDAY: Painted the town RED. All benches wet!

TUESDAY: Boring sunset — added a dash of ORANGE.

WEDNESDAY: Rollered the desert YELLOW. Miles and miles of it!

THURSDAY: Tried out different shades of GREEN on trees etc.

FRIDAY: Colour-washed the sky BLUE — a bit streaky.

SATURDAY: Daubed the evening INDIGO. Deeply satisfying.

SUNDAY: Tidied paintbox.

N.B. Need more VIOLET
     new brush
     sketch pad
     pencils

The Seashell's Prayer

I am whispering.
Are you listening?
Father Neptune,
Hear my plea.

I need you to rock me,
Soothe me,
Set the music
In me free.

Come and save me,
Father Neptune.
I am homesick
For the sea.

Haiku

dawn is delicious

soup made from dew and birdsong

drink it with your ears

Aphrodite

White as dolphins' milk her skin,
Find a shell to place her in.
Grey-green as the waves her eyes,
Cover her to keep her dry.
Gold and soft as sand her hair,
Gentle breezes, blow her there.
Pink as shells her fingernails,
Steer her, fishes, with your tails.
Seas that gave this treasure birth,
Leave your daughter to the earth.

On the Fifth Day ...

"Making birds was fun!
Let's see what's left.
Hmm – legs. No wings though.
Well, OK, forget the wings.
No feathers either. How about
This bit of furry stuff?
And whiskers – could be useful!
Now the beak –
Oops! Just the ones
With nostrils at the wrong end!
Never mind. Here goes!
There – he looks really cute.
I'll call him ... kiwi.
Maybe there's enough
To make another one ..."

Missing

MISSING

HAVE YOU SEEN THIS DOT?

●

small black answers to

Dot or Full Stop

disappeared last Friday

dotnapped?

? and ! both pining

e mail desperate

contact KEYBOARD WATCH

to earn a cash reward

Pillow Monsters

When all is quiet under the duvet
You will hear
The pillow monsters feeding,
Munching dreams
And gobbling snores like truffles.
Nightmares give them indigestion!
Territorial beasts –
Put two together
And a fight is sure to break out.
Then the feathers fly!
A word of warning –
Never feed them after 6 a.m.

Wanted

WANTED a reliable STAR
to lead small party westwards.
Bright with good sense of
direction. No timewasters.
Send CV to CHILDTREK, EARTH.

Rehearsals Rule – OK?

Rehearsals rule – OK?
If you want a concert
Or a Christmas play.

We'll invite
The local Senior Citizens,

We'll delight
Our families and friends,

We don't mind
If we miss most of our lessons,

We'll make sure
It's all right on the day

But till then
Rehearsals rule – OK?

Ghoul School Rules

1. Glide, don't flit!

2. Keep your head ON at all times.

3. No clanking of chains between lessons.

4. No walking through walls. Wait OUTSIDE the classroom.

5. No skeletons to be taken out of cupboards.

6. Line up QUIETLY for the ghost train at the end of the night.

Cleopatra

You
Sun-baked sleeper,
Belly-creeper,
High-heeled walker,
Stealthy stalker,
Four-foot faller,
Caterwauler,
Mobile mouse-trap –
Close the cat flap!

Shocked!

Just look at you –
All studs and rings,
Those false nails
And that fake tattoo!
Your hair! My skirt!
Those boots! That hat!
No, Mum, you're NOT
Going out like that!

The Sweep

Night
is a
chimney
tall and
steep
which
I must
climb to
get to
sleep.

Icicle

long
tooth,
witch's
nail,
tip
of an
ice-
dragon's
tail,
sharp
horn,
drip
that
froze
at the
end of
an ice-
troll's
nose
!

Ass

Ass they all called me
Just part of the furniture,
Never had a name.

Long-ears they called me,
Not the sort of face you'd put
In a fancy frame!

Old friend they called me.
On the road to Bethlehem
That's what I became.

Limerick

There once was a widow from Parma

Who wooed a Peruvian farmer.

She hadn't a horse

And so in due course

They eloped on the back of a llama.

Midnight Feast

A midnight feast!

What shall we take?

Red giant apples,

Meteorite cake,

Slivers of moon,

A salad of stars,

Milky Way coffee

And Jupiter bars!

Jan Dean

Jan Dean lives in Knutsford, Cheshire. Her husband and two sons describe her as 'strange ...', but they have got used to her. She inflicts stories and poems on children and teachers whenever possible and is fanatical about fun! She enjoys cooking and walking the dog – not usually at the same time. She loves singing in the church choir. She is not very good at it, but they are desperate. Her favourite things are: having her feet held, ice cream, and earrings.

It's Not What I'm Used To

I don't want to go to Juniors …

The chairs are too big.
I like my chair small, so I fit
Exactly
And my knees go
Just so
Under the table.

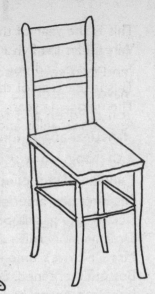

And that's another thing –
The tables are too big.
I like my table to be
Right
For me
So my workbook opens
Properly.
And my pencil lies in the space at the top
The way my thin cat stretches into a long line
On the hearth at home.

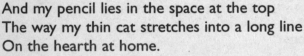

Pencils – there's another other thing.
Another problem.
Up in Juniors they use pens and ink.
I shall really have to think

About ink.

Waiting For

This is the year of the moneybox
When Mrs Da Sylva will play
At holidays and new expensive frocks.
This is the year of the moneybox.
The unlocking year. The year of Paris
And Los Angeles and rubies big as rocks.
Oh, Mrs Da Sylva, cunning as the fox
And thrifty; careful of the last sweet scrape of jam,
Careful as the clever darning of worn socks,
Is taking a hammer to her moneybox.
Sick of saving, sick of prudent locks,
Dreaming of cruise ships waiting in the docks.
Mrs Da Sylva's time has come at last:
Box smithereened. Box withereened.
No more bacon boiled and butterbeaned.
For this is the year.
This the year
This is the year
Of the moneybox.

Granddad In the Garden

My Granddad talks to radishes,
He whispers to the ground
Telling them hot red secrets
So they grow plump and round.

My Granddad sings to lettuces,
Songs for their green hearts,
Watery salad music
For their tender leafy parts.

My Granddad tells tomatoes
Squishy red-nosed jokes.
He whistles sea-shanties to curly kale
And tickles artichokes.

You may think my Granddad's bonkers.
Crazy. Cracking up.
But every year his garden wins
The *Blooming Best* Gold Cup!

Private Rock Pool – KEEP OUT!

I'm the grabber crab
With the quick-draw claw.
Don't you paddle in my pool
'Cos round here I'm the law,
I'm a quick-draw grabber crab
And I'll take you by the toe.
I'll snap my spiky cuffs on you
With a crabby yo-ho-ho!

I'm the snapper crab
With the nippy nippers,
As quick and as sharp
As rose-bush clippers.
Don't dangle feet or fingers here
Dipping digits here is dangerous.
'Cos I'm the fiercest crab alive
HUMUNGOUS, WILD and strangerous!

Beluga, Beluga

Beluga, beluga,
Your echoing song
Swoops through the waves
All the arctic-night long.
Beluga, beluga,
Strange white whale
Sings through the water
Ghostly and pale.

Beluga ... Beluga ...
Your name is a bell
Ringing where emerald icebergs dwell.
Ringing where secrets shine under snow,
Where silver fish shoal and ice-hurricanes blow.
Out of that green and icy sea
Beluga is spinning a dream for me ...

Torches in the Wood

Torches in the wood –
All the trees are like bones
Tall and strange and skeleton thin ...
The cold wind moans.

Torches in the wood –
The small yellow beams
Light the spooky branches
With tiny pinprick gleams.

Torches in the wood –
And hairy scary games
Ghostly owl-hoot voices
Calling out names.

Torches in the wood –
On a wild winter night.
Shivering with pleasure
At each delicious fright.

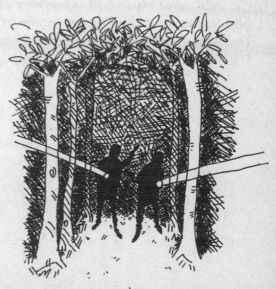

Sweets from Strangers

In the gingerbread house, the gingerbread mouse
Is nibbling away in the walls.
And the gingerbread witch, with liquorice pitch,
Is tarring the roof before the rain falls.

The sugar is sparkling. Each crystal and grain
Is as bright and as sharp as a pin.
Marshmallow cushions plump-pillow the chairs
And the open door whispers 'come in'...
The lemonade's poured. The biscuits are baked.
The whole place is shimmering and fragrant with cake.

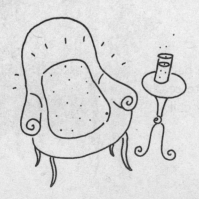

The candyfloss curtains, pretty and pink,
Sway in the honeydew air.
They look so lovely that no one would think
That anything bad could be there.
But don't trust your eyes. For the sugar tells lies
In that diamond glitter, hundreds of flies
Are trapped by the sticky sweet web in disguise.

Each day the witch picks them out with a pinch
Of her long scritch-scratch nails. Tweaks inch by inch
Of the ginger house clean,
So that never a one of those flies can be seen.
Not a hairy black leg.
Not a papery wing.
Not a bluebottle buzz. Not a hint. Not a thing.

She shines up the barley-twist butterscotch hall
And is always quite ready
Should somebody call ...

Who's There?

Nobody breaks the windows,
Nobody spills the milk.
Nobody creeps round the house at night
As silent and secret as smooth black silk.

Nobody digs deep holes in the garden,
Nobody scratches long scars in the wall.
I am afraid of Nobody.
When I'm alone will Nobody call?

Nobody whispers scary stories
To frighten the little ones tucked in their beds.
Nobody growls and makes wicked noises
To make them pull covers over their heads.

When there's just me by myself, I will shudder.
Hush myself. Still myself. Shiver with fear,
Because, in the shadows, I know who is waiting –
Watchful and hungry – Nobody's here …

Nightmare

Now, in the silver-shivery dark
 Invisible creatures howl and bark.
Ghastly goblins,
Horrid hags
Tarantulas and wraiths in rags
Meet upon a midnight hill.
All around the night is still.
Rats scuffle, ravens hover for the kill.
Every speck of night is ripe with death
Ssshh! Be silent – or doom will come and steal away
      your breath …

Shadow Places

It is quiet
In the shadow places.
Quiet
At the edges of things.

The air moves
In strange swirls,
As if invisible dancers
Turn and turn ...

... In the quiet places,
The shadow places,
The grey ghost spaces
At the blurred edge of the world.

Ssh ... [A poem for two actors.]

Ssh ... look behind you.
Ssh ... look ahead.
Ssh ... there's something coming –
Long and creepy,   slow and slimy,   thin and red.

Ssh ... look behind you.
Ssh ... look up there.
There's something weird and scary round the corner
With fangs,   and claws,   and lizards in its hair.

Ssh ... look behind you
There, on that log.
There's something greeny-wriggly, with long and limber legs,
I think that it could be a giant frog.

Ssh ... look behind you
Reflected in the pond beneath the tree ...
It's something weird and horrible –
Something *really* weird and horrible –

That's no spooky monster, stupid!
 – THAT'S ME!

Chinese Water Torture

Chinese Water Torture
Drip Drip Drip.
Can I, can I, Mum
Go on the trip trip trip?

Oh can I, Mum? Please let me go. Go on, Mum –
Mum … pretty please?
I'll even go down on my bended
Knees knees knees.

I'll try wheedling and fawning
From day's end to a new day's dawning.
I'll work on her all morning
While she's waking, stretching, yawning.
I will plead and I will beg
Like a cat twined round her leg
Miaowing and miaowing for a feed.
I'll grumble up to bed
My question nagging in her head
Until she sees how very much I NEED.

..Pleeease mum!

Oh come on, Mum, I promise
I'll never, never ask
For a single other thing my whole life long.
But I've really got to do this.
You just don't understand.
To stop me doing this is cruel. It's wrong.
Everyone will be there.
I'll be the only one
The lonely one that's left behind at home.

tug
tug

Can I, can I, Mum,
Go on the trip trip trip?
Chinese Water Torture
Drip Drip Drip.

Temptation

He'll never miss just one ...
So I took it.
Then I lifted up the box and I shook it.
Seemed as heavy.
Sounded just as full.
All next day I felt that chocolate pull ...

He'll never miss just one ...
So I nicked it.
He'd never, never tell that I had picked it
Peeled the wrapper off and flicked it
Shiny in the bedroom bin.
All next day I knew the chocolate would win

A week on – and he's noticed.
Now he's twigged the box is light
And soon there'll be one big-time fight.
He'll guess who did it – and guess right.
For one and one and one and one
Kept adding on and on and on ...
My last chance – like the chocolate's – gone.

Their Secret is Out!

Teachers are not normal.
Anybody knows that –
Only they pretend to be like us
By shopping in the supermarket
And buying jam and cornflakes.
It's a con.
They don't eat.
They are not real inside their bodies –
They are full of wires and micro-circuits.
They feed on mathematics
And spellings like *psoriasis* and *bouillabaisse*.
Do not believe them when they tell you they were young
    once.
It is a lie.
The factory that makes them
Does not do 'young'.
It only makes three sorts:
Bat-eared,
Needle-nosed,
And Eagle-eyed.

Cold Fish

I've got a killer fish.
At first I liked it —
Swaggering round the tank,
Red and black with fins like battle flags.

Then I won another at the fair.
I slipped it gently to the water,
And it shone like a gold almond.
I watched it nose around the gravel,
Shelter in the weed.

In the morning it was floating
Like a yellow leaf,
While the red fish rammed it
Over and over.

I scooped it out,
But it was too late.

My killer fish swam round and round,
A mean fish with a mean fish smile.

When it dies I'll give away its tank.
I'm off fish.

The Unit of Sleep

I measure fun in grandads —
The best slide in the park is three whole
    grandads long.

I measure ponds in duckfuls —
This is a lake. Tons of ducks. Swans, Green
    mud, good pong.

Picnics are weighed in chocolate biscuits.
Don't care if they do melt, so long as there's
    a lot.

Holidays stretch in miles of sunshine.
Sand, seaslap, shingle. Donkey smell and
    leather. Hot.

Journeys are timed in songs and stories —
From here to Aunt Em's house the wicked
    witch schemes
And as we arrive there the Prince rescues
    Snow White.

The unit of sleep is dreams.

The Rubber Plant Speaks

Mostly they ignore me,
The white plants who walk.
Or bring me water in their leaves.

I wonder how they feed?
With their stubby roots?
And is their green beneath their skins?

Sometimes they talk to me,
But never listen.
They do not recognise my voice.

No one hears. No one hears.
No, not even him,
The little orange plant that swims.

An Owl Flew In My Bedroom Once

My attic bedroom had two windows –
One that opened high above the street
And a skylight – a tile of thick glass
Like a see-through slate.
And through it fell the moonlight
Coring the darkness like an apple-peeler.
Suddenly in that long cylinder of light
Appeared the owl, mysterious and grey
In that cold moon.
He flew in silently – a piece of night adrift –
Escaped. He circled, didn't settle
On the banister or rail.
There was no rattle of his talons,
No gripe or stomp
To make him solid with their sound,
He simply floated in – turned wide – and floated out …
No down or limy dropping
Nothing to prove he'd ever been at all.

An owl flew in my bedroom once, I think.

Dear Mum

I am not happy here.
It's cold and wet and not like Syria at all.
If we can't see the distant hills — that means it's raining.
If we can see them clear — it means the rain's about to fall.

Dear Mum,
There's nothing here worth having.
We're civilising brutish British jerks —
Handing out state-of-the-art technology,
Giving them hypocausts and baths — the works.

We've built some villas, laid some mosaic,
Straightened the winding roads, brought order here.
And in return I sneeze until my nose aches.
We've given up sweet wine for bitter beer.

Dear Mum,
The natives here are fearsome.
They paint their bodies blue — a waste of dye.
The icy wind blows round our knocking kneecaps,
We'll all be turning blue now by and by.

There are no chariot races. There's no circus.
No lions chomping Christians for a joke.
They underpay us and they overwork us,
It makes me want to spit. It makes me choke.

I wish that I was home. I'm off the Empire –
They can stick their army and their eagles too.
As soon as night falls and the rotten rain stops
I'm going to leg it home, dear Mum, to you.

Glass-Eye Charlie

When Glass-Eye Charlie looks at me
I don't know quite what he can see.
I don't know quite how he can spy
Through his shiny blue glass eye.

Does all the world look blue to him?
Or upside-down right through to him?
Maybe I look like a human tadpole
Like I do through granny's front-door peep-hole ...

When Glass-Eye Charlie gives a wink
You ought to hear a bottle-y clink
You ought to see his thoughts swim by
Like fishes in that blue glass eye.

My Sister is Barmy

My sister is barmy about origami.
She's bats about paper squares.
There are peacocks and chickens
And snakes on her bed.
Blue paper tissue fish
Swim down the stairs.
The ceiling is studded
With frogs, stars and roses,
And three-headed monsters
With long curly noses.
She's folded her homework,
She's folded the post,
One morning at breakfast
She folded the toast!
Really it's wrong to blame origami –
If I'm to be honest, my sister's just barmy.

Heart Stuff

Mums and dads they tell you all this stuff
And some of it's OK and some of it is guff.
There's the fairy who takes teeth – that's a story and a half
A sort of magic dentist; gives you cash for fangs – a laugh.
The Father Christmas thing – you know the score –
I've looked out for him, I've squinted out of duvets,
Pretended sleep, but kept watch on the door,
But still I've never seen him. Never will,
My mother says. This Christmas thing, this Jesus stuff
That's strange stuff. Big stuff. After all, a star …
… Not every baby gets a welcome from the sky.
It makes you wonder. Makes you cry
To think what happened then.
If you ask me, I'd say he had it rough.
If he was all that meek and mild, how come he was so
    tough?
Dads and mums they tell you stuff,
Some sticks and some goes in one ear, then out.
They go on, don't they? My mum can't half shout.
But some stuff's special, like this Christmas thing.
You hear it in your heart … sounds daft – it's not, you
    know.
I keep remembering a marvellous baby in the shining snow.

Ghosts in Our Suburban Homes

The creaking of a wicker chair
When something unseen settles there.
It's ghosts, ss, ss, ss,
It's ghosts.
Mad wardrobes swinging in the night,
A flicker at the edge of sight,
It's ghosts, ss, ss, ss,
It's ghosts.
The rocker rocks. The curtains sigh.
Out of the corner of your eye
The solid darkness passes by,
It's ghosts!

They spread themselves along the wall,
Shadows with shadows haunt the hall,
A great grey silent waterfall
Of ghosts!
Come midnight, watch the stair –
Tread sink with no foot there.
It's ghosts, ss, ss, ss,
It's ghosts.
A thousand thousand whispering souls
Mass quietly behind small holes.
A million slither through the cracks
Behind the door, behind our backs,
Insinuating white as wax
Are ghosts!

And in the silence of the moon,
The silver silence of the moon,
The ghosts release a silent tune
To rise like steam from some sad tomb.
The soundless song of frozen skies,
The ice of unsung lullabies,
Wordless as the frosted eyes
Of ghosts.

Ghosts in our suburban homes.
Ghosts in our suburban homes.
Ghosts, ss, ss, ss,
Ghosts.

Angels

We are made from light.
Called into being we burn
Brighter than the silver white
Of hot magnesium.
More sudden than yellow phosphorus.
We are the fire of heaven;
Blue flames and golden ether.

We are from stars.
Spinning beyond the farthest galaxy
In an instant gathered to this point
We shine, speak our messages and go,
Back to the brilliance.
We are not separate, not individual,
We are what we are made of. Only
Shaped sometimes into tall-winged warriors,
Our faces solemn as swords,
Our voices joy.

The skies are cold;
Suns do not warm us;
Fire does not burn itself.
Only once we touched you
And felt a human heat.
Once, in the brightness of the frost.
Above the hills, in glittering starlight,
Once, we sang.

QUEENS GATE SCHOOL
133 QUEENS GATE
LONDON SW7 5LE
TEL 071-589 3587

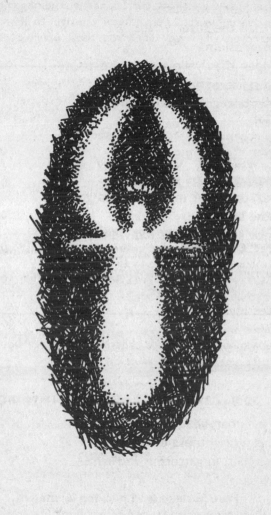

A selected list of poetry books available from Macmillan

The prices shown below are correct at the time of going to press. However, Macmillan Publishers reserve the right to show new retail prices on covers which may differ from those previously advertised.

The Secret Lives of Teachers	0 330 34265 7
Revealing rhymes, chosen by Brian Moses	£3.50
'Ere we Go!	0330329863
Football poems, chosen by David Orme	£2.99
You'll Never Walk Alone	0 330 33787 4
More football poems, chosen by David Orme	£2.99
Nothing Tastes Quite Like a Gerbil	0 330 34632 6
And other vile verses, chosen by David Orme	£2.99
Custard Pie	0 330 33992 3
Poems that are jokes, chosen by Pie Corbett	£2.99
Parent-Free Zone	0 330 34554 0
Poems about parents, chosen by Brian Moses	£2.99
Tongue Twisters and Tonsil Twizzlers	0 330 34941 4
Poems chosen by Paul Cookson	£2.99

All Macmillan titles can be ordered at your local bookshop or are available by post from:

Book Service by Post
PO Box 29, Douglas, Isle of Man IM99 IBQ

Credit cards accepted. For details:
Telephone: 01624675137
Fax: 01624670923
E-mail: bookshop@enterprise.net

Free postage and packing in the UK.
Overseas customers: add £1 per book (paperback)
and £3 per book (hardback).